Sanctuary

Sanctuary

WRITTEN BY

Wendy Marloe

DRAWN BY

Joanna Chen

MARLOE PRESS • NEW YORK • 2015

A sanctuary can be big

or small,

bright

or dark,

open

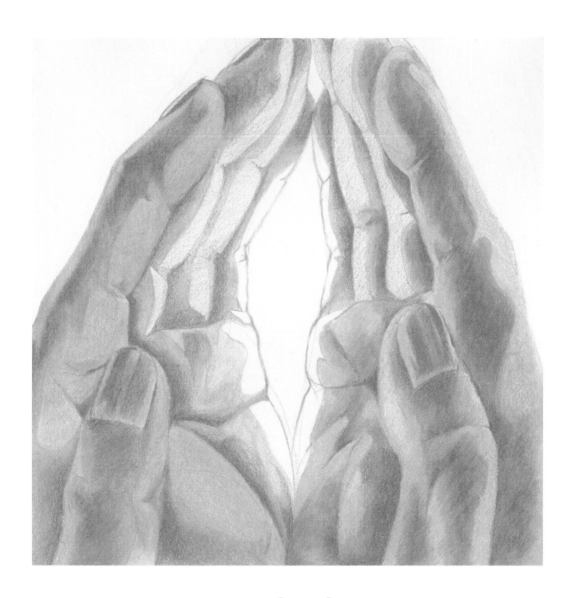

or closed,

hard

or soft.

It can be a place to share

or a place to be alone;

a place that is good for crying

or one that is best for laughing.

It can be round or square, wide or narrow,
short or tall

or it can have no shape at all.

A sanctuary can be noisy

or quiet,

old

or new,

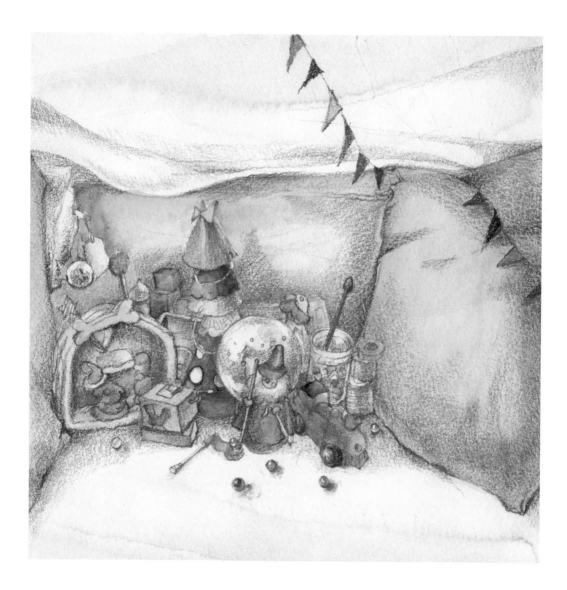

overstuffed

or empty,

one color

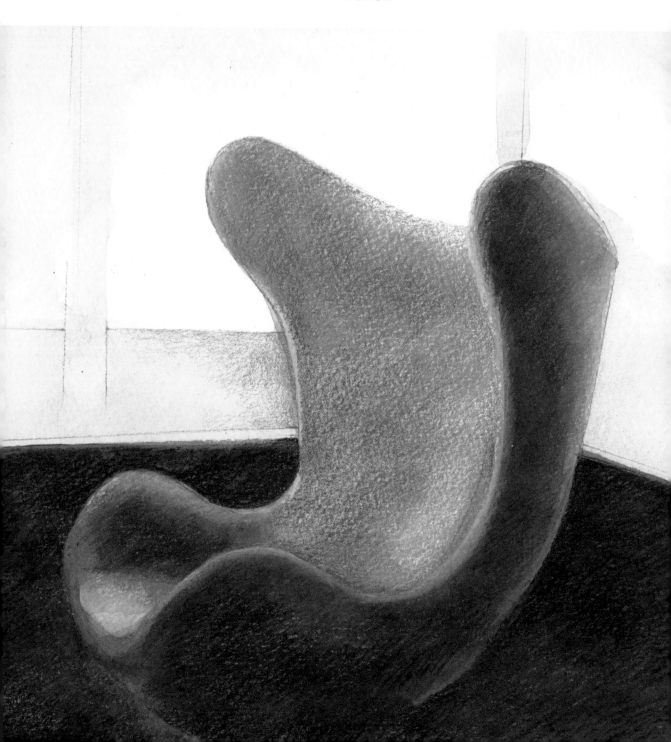

or many.

It can be made out of stone, or cloth,
or cardboard, or wood

or the space between here and the horizon.

It can be a place for speaking

or for listening,

for doing

or for drifting;

a place filled with the works of others

or with the accomplishments of just one.

A sanctuary can be indoors

or out,

well-known

or a secret,

full of razzle-dazzle

or quite plain.

It can be a place for gathering

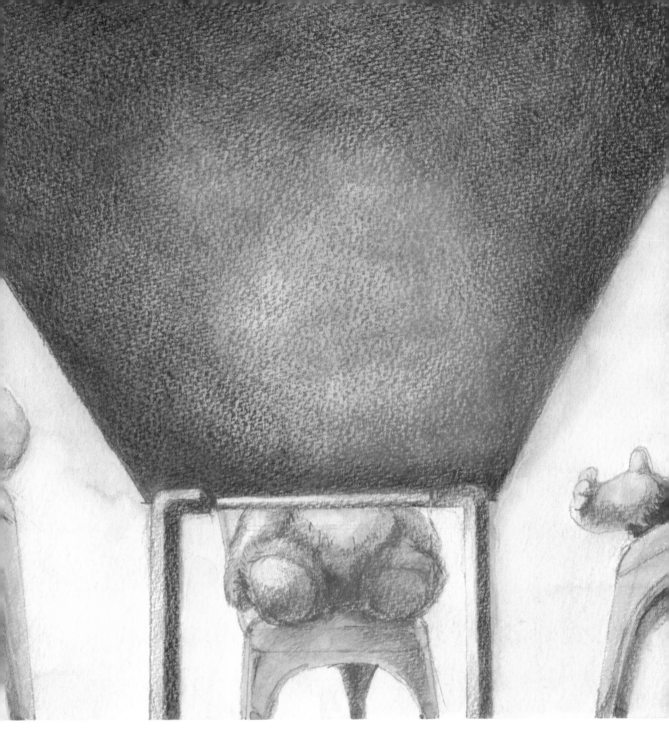

or for hiding,

for singing, or dancing, or splashing, or jumping

or for just sitting quietly;

a place for sunny days

or one to wait out storms.

A sanctuary can be many things.

But most of all, it's yours.

MARLOE PRESS

Text copyright © 2015 Wendy Marloe

Drawings copyright © 2015 Joanna Chen

Printed and bound in the U.S.A.

ISBN 978-0-9823495-3-3

Designed and composed by

Gretchen Achilles/Wavetrap Design

www.marloepress.com